F170

CW00557486

POULTRY FANCIERS' LIBRARY

General Editors

Dr J. Batty   Mrs M. Batty

UNDERSTANDING JAPANESE BANTAMS

OTHER BOOKS AVAILABLE

Understanding Old English Game
Dr. J. Batty

Domesticated Ducks and Geese
Dr. J. Batty

Bantams and Miniature Fowl
W.H. Silk

Managing Poultry for Exhibition
H. Easom Smith

Poultry Colour Guide
Dr. J. Batty and Charles Francis

Pheasants of the World
Dr. Jean Delacour

The Incubation Book
Dr. A.F. Anderson Brown

Guide to Cage Birds
David Alderton

Understanding Indian Game
K.J.G. Hawkey

Understanding Modern Game
Dr. J. Batty and J.P. Bleazard

UNDERSTANDING JAPANESE BANTAMS

By

JOHN K. PALIN

Published by SAIGA PUBLISHING CO. LTD.,
1 Royal Parade, Hindhead,
Surrey, England GU26 6TD

Typeset in 11pt Baskerville by
Inforum Ltd, Portsmouth.
Printed and bound in Great Britain
by Billing and Sons Limited and Kemp Hall Bindery
Guildford, London, Oxford, Worcester

Published by SAIGA PUBLISHING CO. LTD.,
1 Royal Parade, Hindhead,
Surrey GU26 6TD.

Contents

Acknowledgements

We would like to express our thanks to the following for supplying advice and/or photographs: M.E. Wingate, *Poultry World*, A.P. Hollemans, Mr. M. Thick and Mr. F. Kemp.

Reference was made to a number of books, including *Our Poultry* by Harrison Weir and *Bantams* by W.F. Entwisle. A Japanese book (n.d.) was used as a source for some of the illustrations, including the colour, but is has not been possible to trace Baron Takakimi Mitsui— the author— to whom we would like to express our gratitude.

Monochrome Illustrations

Coloured Illustrations

Japanese Bantams

vii

Frontispiece **The Black Red Cock** — this bird exhibits the correct head and tail in accordance with the *standard* of excellence. Bred by the author and regarded as a fine specimen.

Author's Note

In writing this book on Japanese bantams I have drawn from my own personal experience and wish to state here, at the onset, that all I have written is a true account of my associations with the breed.

I hope to interest both existing breeders of this quaint breed of fowl and likewise all others who up to now have only been admirers. Japanese are a true bantam having no counterpart in large fowl.

It is also intended in this treatise on "Japs" to give the reader a clearer view of what constitutes "natural" or Old English Game colours.

When one realises the amount of literature that has been amassed over the last fifty years on exhibition poultry it was with some apprehension that I wished to contribute further to the list. Nevertheless, I observed in conversation with fellow fanciers that the need for a book of this magnitude was desirable for the Poultry Fanciers' Library.

John K. Palin

Sickles — sword shaped, upright,
tall as possible.
Main tail feathers rise above
head by one third of their length.

Numerous soft side-
hangers. These should be
as profuse as possible.

Comb — single, large as possible,
coarse grained with 4 or 5 spikes,
slightly larger in depth than blade.
Must follow line of neck.

Beak well curved.
Eyes large and bright.

Wattles large
and pendent.

Body short
and deep.

Wings to trail on
ground at rear
of body.

Breast very full,
round and carried
prominently forward.

Shanks very short —
almost invisible

Both sexes
very small, lowbuilt, broad and cobby.

Fig. 1.1 **The Ideal Bird.** (Drawn by the author.)

CHAPTER 1

Background and History

TRUE BANTAMS

Having read many books and literature on Japanese bantams I realised that not one of these writers had actually been a breeder or, in some cases, had even seen a Japanese. Much of what was written was conjecture or hearsay.

There have been so many different and varied accounts of the history of these birds that I have come to the conclusion that very little was really known by these authors and still less by the early writers.

It has been repeated again and again that the Japanese bantam arrived on these shores around the mid 1830s and that they are grotesque and not easy to breed or judge. On the other hand, the same writers have bemoaned the fact that there are not more breeders. Needless to say, that is not much encouragement for a breed of fowl that is a credit to the breeder's skill if we are to believe that all fowl are descendants of the Jungle Fowl (*Gallus bankiva*) from South-East Asia.

If the Japanese bantam is grotesque then what category do Modern Game, Naked Necks and Rumpless, to name but a few, come under? The fact is that all have their points of beauty and the enthusiastic breeder of Japanese finds

1

them fascinating. One source calls them "unique, quaint and beautiful."[1]

It is time that someone came to the defence of this breed of fowl. Having been associated with the breed for over forty years, I think that I have enough authority to bring the reader the facts based on my findings as an actual breeder. Also, it should be emphasised that these are **true bantams** whose ancestry can be traced back over 350 years. There are no large Japanese fowl which are the equivalent of the bantam in *type*, but other breeds do exist which are loosely termed "Chabos". They range from birds similar to Aseels to very large Malay-type fowl (Shamos) and, of course, there is the magnificent Long-tailed fowl of Japan, often loosely referred to as the Yokohama of Phoenix, although these birds never achieve the 20–30-foot tail of the true Onagadori fowl in Japan![2]

ORIGINS

Contrary to common belief that the Japanese bantam originated in Japan, there is evidence that this breed of fowl was bred in China for generations before being introduced to Japan. According to Japanese books, these birds are called "Chabos", denoting that they came from South China. It has been estimated that they arrived in Japan between the years 1603 and 1636[3]. Works of art such as

[1] *Book of Bantams*, American Bantam Association, 1975.
[2] See *The Poultry Club Year Book 1967* — in an article entitled *Onagadori* by M.A. Beaumont of Tasmania. Apparently the Onagadori or Long-tailed fowl is bred only in Shikoku, Japan. Mr. Beaumont found no Yokohamas.
[3] *The Chabo and its Breeding*, Inagaki, C., Tokyo, 1951. Quoted by Fred P. Jeffrey in *Bantam Breeding and Genetics*, Saiga Publishing, 1979.

Fig. 1.2 **Silver-Grey Japanese Long-tailed Fowl.**

paintings completed more than 300 years ago depict the Chabo, thus confirming its existence in Japan from the seventeenth century.

Japanese bantams appeared in England and the U.S.A. around 1830 and in Japan around 1600, as noted earlier. These appearances coincided with periods when these respective countries had unrestricted trade with China. Before these dates, no mention or trace of this breed of fowl is to be found in either country.

MISCELLANEOUS NOTES

Much controversy has occurred over the years regarding the size of the comb, tail and legs of the breed. I hope that by the end of this book the reader will have a better understanding of this breed of bantam and will look at it in a more favourable light. There are a far greater number of admirers of Japanese than there are breeders.

Many poultry fanciers keep Japanese as a second string or as a novelty, not really knowing enough or understanding the breed to make it their number one choice. I am not suggesting that the Japanese bantam is an easy breed to manage, far from it. I just want to give the true facts so that the breed is given a fair chance.

There are very few breeders of Japanese in Britain and, because of this, the birds are not plentiful. It is, therefore, a credit to these breeders that some wonderful examples of the breed may be seen at the annual **Japanese Club Show**.

Although the Japanese has been bred for hundreds, maybe thousands, of years it still has not lost its natural instincts, gained from its wild environment. Notice the

4

birds when a shadow falls on them from some passing object—they will sink to the ground and remain immobile until the "danger" has passed.

The female still cackles when she lays her egg to attract her mate in case he has wandered off into the jungle, as was the case with her ancestors, even though he is actually standing beside her in the hen house.

Japanese still persist in taking flight at the slightest movement or disturbance. There are countless other habits which this breed of fowl possesses, even though it has been domesticated for so long. It is unique in the world of poultry in so many ways.

APPEAL OF THE JAPANESE

Japanese bantams are charming birds which lay fairly well and offer a challenge to the dedicated fancier who wishes to breed and show bantams. The short legs and rather tall tail present a striking picture which is almost "statuesque".

Problems in breeding can be overcome by careful selection of stock and by making sure that the birds are quite fit (overfeeding should be avoided). Points to watch are covered later in the book.

Fig. 2.1 **Japanese Bantams.** From a drawing by Ludlow, 1894.
Left: Black Tailed White Cock; *Right*: Black Hen. Note carefully how the standard type has been modified since this drawing from Victorian times.

CHAPTER 2

The Breed Described

THE DETAILED STANDARD

A detailed *standard* now follows which is the official description of the breed.

Standard of Excellence

Although the present *standard* was adopted from the **International Japanese Club** in 1937, the first introduction of the Japanese bantam to the **Poultry Club** *standards* was in 1910.

From this time until the present day, Japanese have, more or less, remained the same; some good, some bad — true bantams of Chinese origin having no counterpart in large fowl. They are a **soft feather breed** with three types of body plumage:

1. Plain feathered
2. Frizzle feathered
3. Silkie feathered

Although "soft feathered", Plain Japanese bantams should not be *excessively* fluffy, their feathers being fairly close to the body, although quite plentiful.

7

Both the male and female of the breed are very small, low built, broad and cobby with a deep full breast and a fully feathered, upright tail. Their appearance is somewhat quaint due to the very large comb, dwarfish character and waddling gait. The plumage should be full and abundant.

The Cock
Head large and broad; beak strong and well curved. Eyes large and bright. Comb single, large and erect and evenly serrated; coarse grained with four or five spikes following the nape of the neck. Earlobes medium size, oval and red. Wattles, pendant and large, coarse grained. Neck short, curving backwards with abundant hackle. Body short, deep and broad. Breast very full, wide and round and carried prominently forward. Wings long with tips touching the ground under end of body. Back very short and wide showing very little daylight between the neck and the tail. Saddle profusely feathered.

Tail very tall, upright — the main tail feathers should rise above the level of the head by about one third of their length, spreading well, with long sword shaped main sickle feathers and numerous soft side hangers.

The tail may just touch the back of the comb but to exceed this point is a fault and the bird would be termed "squirrel-tailed". Thighs very short, not visible. Shanks very short, clean and strong, smooth and sharply angled at the joints; very thick and round. Four toes, straight and well spread.

Weight — 18–20 oz (510–567g approx.)

The Hen
General characteristics should follow closely those described for the cock.

8

Comb well serrated and as large as possible, falling to one side and without defect. Tail well spread and rising above the head. The main tail feathers broad, the foremost pair being slightly curved.

Weight — 18–20 oz (510–567g approx.)

Serious Defects

Narrow build, long legs, long back, wry tail. Tail carried low. Deformed comb and lobed comb in males. High wing carriage. White in lobes. Any physical deformity.

Fig. 2.2 **The Hen.** Note the spread and angle of the tail.

Colours

The number of colours or varieties is tremendous. In Japan there are probably more than twenty main varieties and in the U.S.A. there are sixteen. The *standards* in the U.K. give the following varieties and sub-varieties.

Black Tailed White
Body feathers white. Primaries and secondaries should have white outer and black inner webs. The closed wings look almost white. Main tail feathers pure black, or black with white lacing. Main sickles and side hangers black with white edges. Eyes red, legs yellow.

Black Tailed Buff
Same markings as Black Tailed Whites except that the white is replaced by buff.

Buff Columbian
Rich, even buff; wing primaries and secondaries buff with black inner webs; the closed wings look almost buff. Sickles and side hangers black with buff edges. Neck hackle feathers buff with black centre down each, the hackle to be free from black edges. Eyes red, legs yellow.

White
Pure white without sappiness. Eyes red, legs yellow.

Black
Black with red comb and face. Deep, full black with green sheen. Legs yellow, black permitted on shanks. Soles of feet yellow. Eyes black. (Some of the best blacks have red eyes — author's comment.)

Fig. 2.3 **White Japanese Bantams.** The plumage should be pure white without sappiness.

Greys

Birchen Grey Male: Neck and saddle hackles silver, streaked with black. Breast laced to top of thighs, retaining light shaft to centre of feather. Tail black with green sheen.

Female: Silver laced neck hackle to be clear cut. Back and tail black. Breast feathers laced to top of thighs, retaining light shaft to centre of feather. Lacing to be clear, completely surrounding each feather.

Both sexes have a red face and eye. Both should be a dark red if possible. Legs should be yellow or dusky with a yellow sole.

Silver Grey Male: As Birchen Grey; lacing to be more pronounced.

Female: Colour and lacing as for Birchen Grey. Silvering to extend over back, wings and lower thighs.

Both sexes to have a red face and eyes. Legs to be yellow or dusky with yellow sole.

Dark Grey Male: As Birchen Grey but having a black breast.

Female: As Birchen female but lacking the breast lacing. The breast should be clear black.

Both sexes follow the Birchen Grey in leg and eye colour.

Millers Grey Male and Female: As Birchen Grey but having a mealy breast, as defined in the Poultry Club *standards*.

All Greys must have black secondary wing feathers.

Mottled

Black Mottled: All feathers should be black with white tips. The amount of white may vary, but the ideal is between $3/8$-inch and $\frac{1}{2}$-inch (12–9mm approx). Tail and wings similar but more white permitted.

Blue Mottled: These as the Black, but blue instead of black.
Red Mottled: These as Black Mottled but red instead of black.

In all Mottleds the legs should be yellow or willow. Beaks to match legs. Eyes red or orange.

Blue
Self Blue: All feathers blue, neck feathers may be darker blue than remainder. Legs slate or willow. Eyes orange.
Lavender Blue: All feathers a lavender blue to skin; even shade throughout. Legs slate or blue. Eyes orange or dark brown.

Cuckoo
The feathers throughout, including body, wing and tail, to

Fig. 2.4 **Self Blue Breeding Hen.** Showing the deep, full breast.

be generally uniformly cuckoo coloured with transverse bars of dark bluish-grey on a light grey ground. Legs yellow. Beak yellow marked with black. Eyes orange or red.

Red
All feathers deep red, solid to skin, an even shade throughout. Legs and beak yellow. Both legs and beak may be marked with red. Eyes red.

Tri Coloured
The colours white, black and brown or dark ochre should be as equally divided as possible on each feather. Legs yellow or willow. Eyes red or orange.

Black Red
Wheaten bred. Partridge bred.

Brown Red, Blue Red and Duckwing
The latter four colours as described for Old English Game. (See Chapter 5.)
   The following secondary colours permitted: **Ginger, Blue Dun, Honey Dun, Golden Hackled** and **Furnace**.

Scale of Points

Type	55
Size	15
Condition	15
Colour	10
Leg Colour	5
	100

Fig. 2.5 **Silkie Feathered Japanese Male.** Because of the nature of the feathers the true Japanese type is lost.

These *standards* have since been revised to include the Silkie and Frizzle feathered Japanese varieties which are included below. Suffice to say that the breeders of Japanese will find enough varieties described in this book to keep them fully occupied.

Frizzle Feathered
They shall follow both the type and colour of the plain feathered *standard* but the ends of all the feathers are to curl backward and point towards the head. Feathers must be broad and as closely curled as possible.

Silkie Feathered
This refers to feather construction. All birds must follow

closely the general *standard*, but body feathers shall have a silky, loose feather structure (i.e. feathers have no main centre vein). This cannot apply to primary and secondary wing feathers, or to true tail feathers, which would nullify any true Japanese type.

JUDGING

As shown in Chapter 5, when considering the quality of a Japanese bantam the emphasis should be on the superlative: *very — very* tall tail, *very* tiny body and so on. This approach should leave little opportunity for inferior birds to be treated as champions. However, a correctly "balanced" bird is vital; for example, a very tall tail on an untypical bird should not be regarded as a feature worthy of a prize, thus ignoring all other features.

The stages involved in judging are as follows:

Stage 1

When judging Japanese, first look at the bird overall and in particular note the following:

a)   carriage of the bird;
b)   height of breast;
c)   width of breast;
d)   shortness of back;
e)   length of feather in tail;
f)   carriage of wings.

Stage 2

Then take the bird in the hand and establish:

a)   length and colour of legs;
b)   colour of plumage;
c)   size and texture of comb and wattles;
d)   condition of the bird;
e)   any defects or departure from the *standards*.

Avoid Prejudice

Far too many judges are biased and give preference to varieties of their own choice. All varieties should be judged according to the *standards* and given a fair crack of the whip.

CHINESE IMPERIAL BANTAMS

I have often been asked in the past about the **Chinese Imperial bantam**. An article regarding this breed appeared some years ago in *The Field* magazine. These birds were supposedly owned by the Dowager, the Empress of China, in the 1800s.

The birds depicted in the article were similar to inferior long-legged Japanese bantams. Around this period of the mid-1800s, when prettily feathered fowls were being imported from the orient, they were reported on by the press.

It must be surmised that the bulk of the imported birds, which eventually reached these shores, were the second-rate specimens as regards appearance. Nevertheless, these

17

birds would have contained in their make-up the potential to breed offspring equally as good as their ancestors, and in the clever hands of poultry fanciers of that era this was achieved. It was quickly realised that the peculiar leg factor was eminent in the breed named the Japanese bantam; one of the many breeds of fowl that arrived from the East.

From information received from Japan, where this quaint fowl was bred to a pattern, it appeared that, even though its rather ostentatious adornments — head, tail, feather and colour — were much sought after, the most important feature of the bird was its legs which, of necessity, had to be as short as possible. Breeders of these birds in Britain, being aware of the importance of the short leg, soon adopted the same standard, and now, some 100 years later, this is still considered to be the most important part of the bird. Without short legs this bantam would not be a true Japanese. However, I believe that, even without the short leg, this bird retains its type.

Over fifty years ago the majority of bird gardens were privately owned and, according to fashion, each vied with the other to obtain the most rare and unusual birds. Naturally, birds from the orient were much prized, especially the tiny feathered fowls from China.

The British aristocracy, having the necessary connections, would associate with such celebrated personalities as the Empress of China. As a result, the rare and exotic birds sent as gifts inevitably included the tiny Japanese bantam. Often the press, or some other mistaken person, named the birds after their owner; for example, the Chinese Imperial fowl.

Even today when bird gardens are open to the public, I have often seen Japanese bantams in the enclosures looking very pretty and of obvious Japanese type but, unfortunately, very few are endowed with the necessary short leg required to make them a true Japanese. Similarly, many birds advertised for sale as Japanese, although of definite type bodywise, have again been lacking in the low carriage of the true Japanese.

Although there is no harm in aquiring these birds as pets, if one wishes to go that step further and enter the world of exhibitions only the true, short-legged type must be entertained.

If anyone desires to keep long-legged Japanese, these birds could easily be termed Chinese Imperial bantams although there is no recognised *standard* for them.

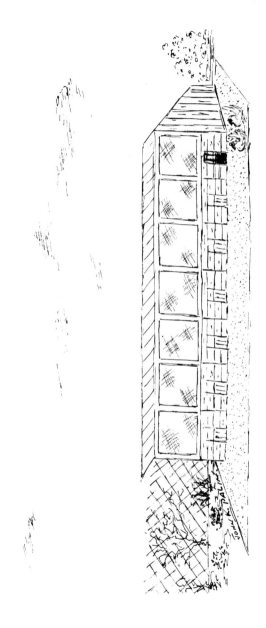

Fig. 3.1 **Range of Pens** — these may be provided with covered runs at either front or rear.

CHAPTER 3

Housing and Management

IDEAL ACCOMMODATION

Accommodation for Japanese bantams varies depending on the space the proposed fancier has at his disposal. The ideal type of bantam house will be described first. This should consist of small units of a similar pattern side by side with a small covered run at the front of each house. These need not be large; in fact, small units and runs are preferable for this breed.

Size and Shape

Houses should slope from front to back with the top half of the front covered with $\frac{1}{2}$-inch mesh wire netting. The lower half should be boarded in with a pophole provided. This ensures that the birds will only receive fresh air. Draughts are fatal to any kind of livestock. Make sure that houses face south if possible.

The house part should be approximately 3 feet (0.9m approx.) from back to front, 4 feet (1.22m approx.) wide and 4 to 5 feet (1.22–1.52m approx.) in height at the front, sloping to about a foot lower at the rear. Access may be from a door at the rear or at the front depending on the situation.

Run

Each house should have its own run at the front. These need only be about 5 or 6 feet (1.52–1.83m approx.) long and it is advisable to cover the top of the runs with corrugated perspex to keep out the wind and rain. In certain parts of the country bad weather conditions can be severe and prolonged.

All runs should be covered with ½-inch mesh netting to keep out the vermin, i.e. mice and sparrows, both of which carry disease and consume and foul the bantams' food.

Where the proposed breeder of Japs has only a flagged or concrete area he need not despair. The bantam house-cum-scratching shed is ideal for Japanese. These may be wire meshed completely at the front, sloping inward from the top to bottom thus ensuring that the rain cannot penetrate into the house.

Alternatively, a single building of either brick or timber of similar proportions and of any length desired may be sectioned off.

If, however, space is limited then practically any kind of building is suitable provided it is **dry and free from draughts**.

The Large Unit

If a fancier has a large building available, the floor may be divided into pens about 6 feet square (1.83m² approx.) with two or three nest boxes in various positions in each as required. These pens will accommodate a trio of Japanese bantams nicely, or a hen with chicks or, equally well, a number of growing stock.

As an alternative to this arrangement, rabbit hutch-type accommodation may be arranged around the walls of the large unit. These may vary in size from one of 2 feet by 3 feet (0.61 by 0.9m approx.) to a larger hutch measuring 4 feet by 6 feet (1.22 by 1.83m approx.). According to the size selected, this type of accommodation will be suitable for either single birds or breeding pairs.

It is possible to use large houses and, therefore, keep a greater number of birds together. However, Japanese bantams are usually healthier and better fertility is achieved if the birds are housed as previously described.

Guard Against Predators

It must be pointed out that whatever type of accommodation is provided, it is essential that houses are either lifted clear of the ground or, alternatively, that wire netting is firmly fixed around the base. So many birds have been lost to the ravages of rats or foxes that protection in this area is essential. If a cat can walk under the houses upright then you have no fear of predation by rats.

Try for a Pleasing Appearance

No matter what kind of units are used there is no reason why they should detract from the pleasant appearance of the garden or establishment. Some simple landscaping, particularly the use of trees or shrubs, can make a unit very attractive.

As already suggested the houses should face south to

enable the stock to get the full benefit of the sun and fresh air. By fixing up some screen or trellis-work to support climbing plants, such as roses, honeysuckle or clematis, the units can become a pleasing feature of the garden. A lawn or flower bed at the front of the pens can also enhance their appearance.

INTENSIVE SYSTEM

Where Japanese bantams are the fanciers' selection of fowl, small gardens have the advantage over large acreage. It is one thing to keep fowls, but quite another to breed and understand them. Only by using the intensive system for these birds can the fancier have complete satisfaction in his hobby.

There are undoubtedly great advantages in keeping poultry on unrestricted open range: economy in food, housing and so on, but the Japanese bantam cannot endure these conditions for long. It may be possible for a time in the south of England, but even there, in sheltered positions, this breed will deteriorate eventually.

I have known countless numbers of Japanese fanciers who have exposed their birds to these conditions, but none have lasted very long, unless they continued to reintroduce new strains as their own birds deteriorated. If conditions had been suitable this deterioration would not have come about. The truth of the matter is that these fanciers do not fully understand the breed. To compare these birds with other more conventional breeds of bantam is ridiculous. Just as the Japanese is dissimilar in appearance to other bantams so must its habitat be different.

Fig. 3.2 **Penning Room** — this should not detract from the pleasant appearance of the garden. The adjoining run, shown above, can be used to assess individual birds.

Comfort Essential

It is not intended here to decry the use of free range but this method of keeping birds must be put to good use and in a sensible manner which is conducive to the birds' requirements. It would be sacrilege to submit Japanese to bleak windswept open spaces, gales, freezing rain, fog and snow no matter how accommodating the roosting houses may be. By housing Japanese bantams as advocated in this book, the birds will thrive.

Incidentally, these remarks also apply to various other breeds of ornamental bantams.

CAGES

Bantams are often kept in show cages for a considerable length of time and on the door being opened they may refuse to leave. On being taken out of their cages and let loose in the garden they have wasted no time in returning to their cages again. This proves that most birds are quite content to stay wherever they are fed and watered, provided that they are comfortable.

It is a recognised fact that such birds as canaries and budgerigars, described as "cage birds", breed and live happily for many years confined in this way. Why, then, should bantams not be kept in a similar manner? They have been domesticated as long as many other species of livestock and, provided that they are fed and watered regularly and kept clean, there is no reason why these birds cannot be kept as other cage birds are.

The point being emphasised here is that Japanese ban-

tams are small with short legs and the accommodation must be suitable for their physical appearance and temperament. Therefore, small compact units are ideal for these birds to keep them in sound, healthy and active condition.

A clean, well laid out unit is much better than a large house which has stagnant water and dirty conditions. Conditions such as these are disastrous to any kind of poultry and **especially to small bantams**.

Of course, there are always exceptions. Some bantam fanciers never make the grade of good stockmen through the lack of common sense, no matter how neat their layout.

Fig. 3.3 **Cages.** The interior of the penning room showing the cages. These birds are ready to be transported to breeding houses.

Protection

One last thought on housing: no matter what kind of wooden building is utilised, make sure it receives a liberal application of creosote inside and out and repeat this every two or three years.

FLOOR LITTER

Having now acquired some idea of what constitutes suitable accommodation for Japanese bantams the next step is to choose floor litter.

Cleanliness is next to godliness and this applies to poultry houses, although it appears quite a number of poultry fanciers do not agree with this old adage.

Floor litter is available in different forms. It may be sawdust, shavings, sand, soil or peat; all of which are suitable in some respects, but each has its drawbacks. Where the climate is fairly dry, sand and soil are preferable. Alternatively, sawdust is advised where the weather is usually damp. Peat moss is very good being very absorbent and not quite as dusty as sawdust. However, it is inclined to stain light coloured plumage.

If the right kind of litter is used and kept dry, it may be used for a very long time provided it is put through a sieve and all droppings removed frequently. I find that by adding new litter to old the birds are not unduly disturbed by the change in environment.

Whatever kind of litter be provided for Japanese it is vital that it is thoroughly dry. It has been suggested to me that litter of a damp nature is necessary for retaining the yellow leg. *This is quite wrong!* Having experimented over many years with various types and conditions of floor covering, I conclude that nothing but trouble can come from damp litter. Leg colour depends on strain and feeding.

Not only must the litter be dry but it must also be easily crumbled, for caked litter and droppings, even in a dry state, can harbour lice and disease and must be moved frequently. Nothing smells worse than a damp poultry house, the poisonous fumes arising from the wet litter are most detrimental to the birds and their owners.

AVOID OVERCROWDING

It has often been said that by putting a number of birds together during the winter months they will keep much warmer and can endure the long, cold nights. My own personal experience has been the reverse where Japanese are concerned. Two or three birds to each 4 by 3 feet unit or three or four birds to one slightly larger unit is recommended. In fact, I often keep birds on their own all the year round and these do much better than birds crowded together.

I once believed that birds with discoloration in their combs were, as most poultry books advocated, suffering from liver disease. Maybe a diseased liver does cause a discoloured comb but it is important to discover what causes the diseased liver in the first place. After much experiment and observation I am inclined to suspect that it is overcrowded conditions.

As previously suggested, lack of fresh air, overcrowding and damp are harmful and these conditions cannot be in any way beneficial to Japanese bantams.

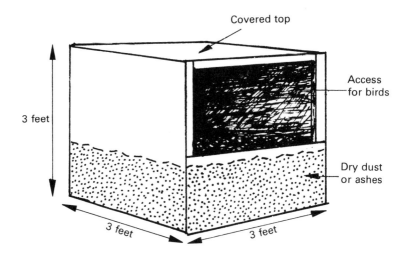

Fig. 3.4 **Dust Bath.** It is important that no rain should be allowed entry into the box to wet the dry earth.

DUST BATH

All fowl require a dust bath and none more so than Japanese. If the litter is kept dry and clean the birds will sometimes indulge several times a day. This is the natural way for many birds to cleanse themselves from insect vermin. I have seen Japanese chicks a few days old enjoying a dust bath on warm sunny days; a sure sign of contentment. It is surprising how much dust the feathers can hold until the birds stand up and thoroughly shake themselves, removing any mites at the same time.

PERCHES

No mention of perches may lead one to believe that I do not approve of such. After much thought and study I find it a very debatable point as to whether perches are suitable for the true Japanese with the required short leg. Even in most breeds with normal structure, early perching may cause a dented keel bone.

Breast bones are very pliable in young birds but as they mature the bone hardens; at a young stage, however, they are liable to damage that can be irreparable. Even game birds that have long shanks to rest their breasts on may dent the bone at this stage of development.

Japanese bantams, being of unusual structure and having such short legs and broad breasts, have no alternative but to sit on the perch with the whole weight of the body on the breast bone. Even if the perch is very broad the bird will be inclined to sit on the edge with the same consequences. At no time in the life of a true Japanese will its legs ever be able to support fully the weight of its body whilst perching.

ESSENTIAL REQUIREMENTS

Other appliances required are food and water vessels. These should be of the kind that can be easily cleaned. Earthenware pots with a lip, sold in any pet shop, are ideal food hoppers for Japanese. Various sizes can be purchased which are suitable for chicks or adults; the lip round the edge prevents the food being scattered about. For drinkers it is best to use the plastic hook-on type; these are hygienic and can be scalded at regular intervals. This removes any foreign matter or bacteria that may form on the inside of the vessels. Paste pots make excellent drinkers for chicks.

CHAPTER 4

Feeding

EFFECT OF DIET

Purity of strain is usually regarded as being more important than any other factor. Nevertheless, it has been realised that **feeding** plays just as important a part as blood lines. The two must go hand in hand.

Every year some fanciers bemoan the fact that they have had a bad season, yet in the same area others are experiencing the opposite situation with similar stock and sometimes with birds of the same strain.

Birds refusing to feed, clear eggs, dead in shell, infertile birds and youngsters dying at the crucial two to three week old stage are all symptoms of a bad season. Unpredictable weather may be the reason for the breeder's dilemma, but more often than not improper and inadequate feeding is the main cause.

The first essential in the breeding pen is **fitness**. The right birds should have already been selected for type, colour and other requirements, but no matter how good they are in these respects, without fitness they are useless. Fitness can only be put there by the breeder and unless strict regard to the requirements of the birds is followed then the health of the stock in general will suffer.

To have healthy birds is essential at all times, but all birds

33

intended for the breeding pen must be 100% fit, otherwise the breeders will just be wasting their time. Even with stock in the finest condition, a fancier will breed a percentage of birds not suitable for breeding or exhibition. However, provided all chicks are healthy when hatched the breeder should not be too disappointed.

More important than what you *give* a chick is what it actually *eats*. All poultry should be well fed, none more so than growing chicks. Even if the chick has a full crop it should always be looking for a bit more.

At the same time, never leave food lying about; any that is uneaten after the birds have moved away should be removed.

Fig. 4.1 **Chicks Feeding** – a Black Tailed White hen with her clutch of two month old chicks.

Overfeeding

Probably, more birds die due to overfeeding than under-feeding. There is a vast difference between a *fit* bird and a *fat* bird. Birds fed sparingly are much fitter than birds fed *ad lib*. Many Japanese bantams given access to food at all times tend to eat less and less and, eventually, fade away and die.

Birds are not underfed if they remain fit and healthy. Well kept birds may live up to sixteen or even eighteen years of age and hens may rear and hatch chicks at this age.

Only sitting hens should have food put before them at all times as they are able to eat only a few grains a day — roughly a good handful per week.

Feeding Chicks

Contrary to what some breeders and authors advise, hard-boiled egg finely chopped is an excellent food with which to commence feeding chicks, and can be recommended, as can chick crumbs. After all, the only food in a chick's body on emerging from the shell is the yoke of the egg. However, it must be stressed that all food must be given in moderation. A good stockman who really understands his birds soon learns just what the chicks require and feeds them accordingly.

Sometimes grower's mash may be used in place of egg. However, in feeding Japanese the fancier must be very careful over what kind of mash is given. Mash containing grass or fish meal is too stimulating for chicks and the only mash suitable is milk mash; this may cost a bit more

Fig. 4.2 **Three Week Old Chicks.** Here we see a Birchen Grey hen with a clutch of three week old Black Tailed White chicks. Their feeding at this stage is of the utmost importance.

but nevertheless it is cheaper in the long run. Chick crumbs manufactured in the same way are the only ones that should be used.

The egg food should be discontinued after the first week, as by this time the chicks will be strong enough to eat other foods. Chick crumbs either moistened with water or cod-liver oil can now be fed until the young are three or four months of age.

On alternate days it is advisable to feed crushed oats, ground fine in an old mincer, together with onions and greens that have also been through the mincer. Japanese need protein to promote feather growth, but forcing food should not be given.

At the same time the diet should not be restricted to keep down the size of the birds. We do not want large birds by any means, but at the same time we must have substance. The tiniest specimens are usually weakly and not fit to be included in future breeding.

For the last meal of the day crushed grain may be fed. This takes longer to digest so it remains in the crop longer and sustains the bird through the night. It is generally known that hard feather breeds require hard food, and soft feather breeds require soft food, but all fowl require a certain amount of grain in their diet.

Japanese require a yellow leg and though this must come from the breeding stock a limited quantity of split corn enables this colour to be retained. Too much, however, can affect the plumage of white breeds and, for this reason, it must be fed sparingly.

Meat is very good for Japanese, encouraging feather growth. Dried meat sold in pet shops for dogs is ideal, when finely chopped and added to the mash once or twice weekly.

Vitamin A is found chiefly in carrots and cod-liver oil, so these are imperative additives to the diet of birds bred intensively.

The food mentioned here as being suitable for Japanese contains all the vitamins required for poultry, especially A, B and D. Vitamin deficiency is the cause of many ailments in bantams.

"Variety is the spice of life" and, bearing this in mind, it is necessary to give chicks little extras like canary seed, linseed and hempseed. Just a pinch now and again makes a difference in their tiny lives and puts a shine on their plumage.

In connection with food, remember the following rules:

1. **Do not stint your feeding. Never feed for smallness, breed for it.**
2. By the time the chicks are three to four months old they should be taking the same feed as the adults. Feed mash in the morning and grain in the evening: twice a day is sufficient. Sometimes a meal may be missed depending on the condition of the birds.
3. Any table scraps or green food should be minced or finely shredded and incorporated into the mash. This ensures that all the birds get an equal share of everything, if fed separately they pick out the things they like and leave the rest.

Listed below are some foods often given to poultry that are not recommended for Japanese:

fish	tomatoes
pastry	potatoes
beetroot	peas
all kinds of fruit	rhubarb

They are not necessary either cooked or raw.

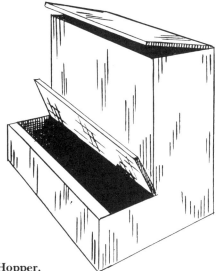

Fig. 4.3 **Grit Hopper.**

GRIT

Whether grit should be given greatly depends on the other constituents of the diet, as birds often obtain sufficient calcium from proprietary food supplies. However, from observations of birds with access to outside pens I believe that Japanese should be given a trace of flint grit about once a week.

All food given must be fresh and wholesome at all times. The golden rule is always to feed when the birds are keen for their food. Overfeeding kills. Feather plucking and egg eating will be unheard of if the birds are fed as outlined above.

WATER

Water should be supplied to Japanese from birth. It is imperative, however, that this is replaced and is fresh daily. It is wrong to deny chicks water — all chicks bred on an open range will be seen to drink the dew off the grass from the day they are born. I have never known any harm come to a chick with access to water, provided the water was clean and fresh. However, I have seen disastrous results from water that was fouled and dirty. If you supply your birds with water you could not drink yourself you need never worry about the condition of your stock.

These remarks are mainly for newcomers to the fancy. Experienced fanciers will of course have their own particular methods of feeding. Everything I have written on the feeding of these birds has resulted from my own experience over many years and my losses have been very few compared to other breeders I have known.

One last thought — it must be appreciated that a fancier can feed the finest food in the world but this can never make an inferior bird into a champion.

THE MOULT

The annual moult is a natural phenomenon and, even though the Japanese bantam for its body size has the largest wealth of feather of any fowl, there should be no cause for alarm during this period. If the birds are fed correctly and breeding has finished by the end of June or July at the latest there is no reason why they should experience any difficulty during the moult.

A quick moult is essential and the more feathers discarded the better. If everything goes well, four or five weeks should see the birds with their new plumage. Wrong feeding and late breeding are two of the main reasons for any difficulties or problems during the moult.

Many poultry books advocate special and extra food during the moult. This is not recommended; wild birds receive no extras and all appear to perform this natural function without any undue stress. The wild birds pick up a variety of foods and the reader of this book will surely appreciate that the foods recommended earlier are suitable for the well being of the birds at all times.

However, it should be realised that males generally have more difficulty than females during the moult. Being such an enormous drain on the constitution, the loss and renewal of plumage on well feathered males is a most critical time and, unless correct management ensues throughout the bird's life, many good specimens will be lost.

During this period the comb of the bird is also affected. Combs and wattles shrivel and lose size and texture. This condition of the head sometimes persists until the beginning of the breeding season.

Fig. 5.1 **Type comes First!** Although colour is important in determining variety, it is the adherence to *type* that denotes the breed. Here we see

CHAPTER 5

Type and Colour

In the Fancy it is usual to state that: **type comes first and this makes the breed, whereas colour is secondary, this indicating the variety**.

MEANING OF TYPE

The **type** of any bird or animal is what one can see with the eye. In Japanese bantams body shape is the one part of the bird that is stable. It is the exaggerated adornments that are hard to come by. In Japan the birds are bred for individual points. This is not confined to the birds themselves, but applies to different parts of the country. For example, breeders in one part of Japan will concentrate on breeding for head points, in another part breeders select birds with excellent tails, whilst in yet another part the birds are bred for colour.

In Britain, the U.S.A. and many other countries, however, all these fancy and unusual qualities are required in the *one* bird. Quite a tall order for such a tiny bantam. Throughout the process of judging **very** is the operative word; *very* tall tail, *very* large comb, *very* short back, *very* short leg, *very* tiny body. All this adds up to *very hard to breed*, but very gratifying when once achieved.

43

Comb

The **comb** is the part of the bird that conjures up the term "grotesque". Without a large comb the Japanese would loose its type and nothing looks worse than a small comb. The ideal comb has four or five spikes, upright in the male, optional in the female. The spikes and blades should be equal in depth and coarse grained.

Tail

At the opposite end of the Japanese bantam is the hall-mark of a true bird — **that tall, towering tail**.

Some years ago the emphasis amongst breeders was on wealth of feather and the question of tail carriage was

Fig. 5.2 **The Comb.**

paramount. The controversy raged for many years, both here and in America, with the outcome being that it was agreed that tail carriage should be more forward than perpendicular. Although the present British Japanese Bantam Club have once again insisted on the upright tail, many fanciers believe this is not the best type of Japanese bantam.

It is very easy to breed the birds with the upright, whip tails. These can be seen to lack wealth of feather when compared to the well spread, slightly forward tails. Usually, the best tails just touch the back of the comb; a more forward carriage than this is termed "squirrel tailed" and is a serious fault.

The ideal Japanese hen is required to have a well spread tail so why not the cock? As explained to one lady fancier when viewing a winning hen at a club show, if the hen had had sickles it would have been squirrel tailed; she saw the point. If a judging stick is placed in line with the perfect female tail the principle being established may be seen quite easily.

In fact, when following the *standard* the tail cannot be completely perpendicular if the main sickles are slightly curved. In the ideal tail the two main sickle feathers should start to rise from the base of the neck hackle (on a good specimen), curve slightly towards the head and finish with the tips of the sickles in line with the back of the comb.

Although a squirrel tail is bad, soft sickles are worse and a dropped tail is unthinkable in this breed.

Body

Breeders with an eye on heads and tails tend to neglect

body width. As already stated, body shape tends to be consistent in profile, but narrow build is very prevalent in today's Japanese bantams. Width of the breast is most important both from the looks and a respiratory point of view and birds should be selected that excel in this respect.

The broad, round front of both sexes enhances the **type** of a Japanese to a great extent. Breeders must bear this in mind at all times.

The length of back in these birds should appear to be "nil". The neck and the tail should commence from the same point, thereby eliminating any possibility of the appearance of a back.

Legs

Last, but by no means least, remains the factor which makes or mars the type of a Japanese bantam; this being the **length and thickness of the legs**. These must be as short as possible, smooth and closely scaled, but more important still is their thickness. A thin, narrow leg is a sign of weakness and should be avoided at all times.

A short, thick leg is difficult to obtain, being a mutation of the natural leg length. It is supposed to be bred on a ratio of one short to three long, but it is believed that the more inbred and purer the strain, the greater the chance of breeding a strain with short legs. In any event, modern research has indicated a different proportion as indicated in Chapter 6.

I hope that these remarks convey to the reader a clearer picture of what is required in the type of a Japanese bantam.

Note

When Japanese chicks are about two weeks old, look for the ones with the longest backs. Those that look like boats will, when mature, have the shortest length in back. Many discard this type of young bird, believing they are contrary to the *standard* and this has been their undoing.

COLOURS

Japanese bantams are to be seen in many colours. Notes on these are now given to supplement the standards given earlier.

Note

The Japanese Bantam Club has now recognised the inclusion of an "off colour" class at the Club Show, thus coming into line with the views of many fanciers. Also, a class for the true Birchen Grey has been recognised and all other greys are to be entered in the class for off colours.

Black Reds

In Japanese bantams, Black Reds have three variations which are described below.

Dark Red

The Black Breasted Red has a dark red hackle striped with black, crimson shoulders and black wing bays, known as "Crow Wing". The hen being black with dark red hackle striped with black.

Fig. 5.3 **Pair of Black Red Wheaten Bred Japanese.**

Black Red Partridge Bred
Second is the Partridge Black Red, similar to the Black Breasted Red but with dark, bay-coloured wing ends. Female — back, shoulders and wings even partridge brown stippled with fine dark markings, golden neck hackle striped with black. Salmon coloured breast shading to ash-grey belly, primary and tail feathers dark.

The frontispiece depicts a Partridge Black Red cock bred by myself. Even though the photograph is in black and white one may see the bay coloured wing ends.

Black Red Wheaten Bred
The last of the three variations is the Wheaten Black Red

48

with its light red neck and saddle hackle, and sound light coloured wing bays. The hen is wheaten coloured with straw coloured hackle and dark coloured tail feathers. The Wheaten Black Red is actually a distinct variety from the other two varieties and is in the buff family.

Hackle and shoulder markings are, in most fowl, even self coloured, but are not seen until such times that unusual conditions, such as strong sunlight, bring out these points, some being most pronounced. I have bred all these three colours of Black Red Japanese and all had excellent type.

Buffs

The ancestor of all varieties of Japanese bantams is the Black Pointed Buff. Even now, after hundreds of years of specialist breeding, Blacks, Whites, Wheaten Black Reds and Brown Reds still crop up in clutches of Buffs, provided one breeds enough! As there are only a few breeders in this country, coloured Japanese are very scarce, barely managing to keep the stud going from season to season.

Buffs are a beautiful variety (the reference is to Black Tailed Buffs of course).

Columbian

Regarding the Columbian with the striped hackle, these are quite rare in Buffs. Actually the Black Tailed Buff is Columbian with the striped hackle bred out. Columbian is the natural colour for all black pointed fowl. Two typical examples are Light Sussex and Columbian Wyandottes.

We see the dark ticking appearing from time to time in the neck hackle of both Black Tailed Whites and Buff Japanese — a very bad fault.

49

Fig. 5.4 **Black Tailed Buff Cockerel.**

Piles

Piles have cropped up in the breeding of Buffs and Black Reds but have lacked the wing bays. It is very easy to attain hackle and shoulder markings but much harder to get the bay coloured wing ends.

Duckwings

Duckwings are difficult to breed (although the odd male has turned up in experimental breeding). True coloured Duckwing females are very rarely seen.

Males are seen at shows and in other breeders' yards, but are usually of poor type, more like Leghorns than Japanese. The best came from Yorkshire — fair in type but lacking the true coloured wings from which the name is derived; i.e., blue wing bar and white coloured wing bays. These were probably bred from Black Breasted Greys without lacing.

Greys

Greys are very scarce today, though, at one time, they were the most popular. They are very lovely birds and I have bred some beautiful Greys both for colour and type.

Four varieties are recognised and this has possibly been their downfall. They are:

1. Dark Grey or Black Breasted
2. Mealy (or Millers) Breasted
3. Birchen Grey (the true Grey with the silver laced breast)

Fig. 5.5   **Birchen Grey Cockerel.**

4. Silver Grey

All have silver neck and saddle hackle, silver shoulders and wing bows and black wing bays. Females are sooty black with varying degrees of silver on hackle and breast.

The Mealy Breasted Grey is regarded by some as a "mongrel" being a cross between a grey and some other variety, i.e. a Black Tailed White crossed with a Grey.

The Black Breasted Grey is not stable as regards colour and cannot be relied on to breed true.

Some fanciers believe that the Mealy and the Black Breasted varieties should not be recognised. It would appear that these two varieties have been the reason why very few good Grey Japanese are seen today.

Fig. 5.6 **Silver Grey Pullet.**

Brown Reds

Brown Reds are similar to Birchen Greys with the laced breast and hackles, yellow or orange colour being substituted for the silver. Brown Reds are only recognised with the laced breast so why not Greys?

Both these varieties should follow the colours for Birchen and Brown Red Modern Game bantams. The Brown Red and Birchen Grey Japanese are two of the most beautifully coloured varieties and worth a place in any fancier's establishment.

Fig. 5.7 **Brown Red Cockerel.**

Plate 1

A White   C Black
B Black Tailed Buff   D Black Mottled

Plate 2

A Buff Mottled
B Black Tailed White

C Blue
D Partridge Black Red

Self Colours

Japanese bantams are standardised in four self colours:

1. Reds
2. Blacks
3. Whites
4. Blues

Reds are stated in the *standards* as having all plumage deep red. Although I have never seen a Japanese with all red feathers, I have bred Deep Reds from Black Tail Buffs. These of course had black tail and wing feathers.

There are a number of red breeds in poultry — Sussex, Rhode Island Reds, Frizzles, etc., but all have black in tail and wings which is the natural colour pattern. I doubt if there are any red Japanese, have been or ever will be.

Blacks, Whites and Blues are established and are usually sports from other varieties, but can also be bred true to colour.

Blacks are the strongest variety and, provided one obtains the right birds from a reliable source, a stud can be formed that can last for years. They are lovely birds and usually have wonderful type and an abundance of feather. Poultry Club *standards* state the colour of eyes to be black; many of the best blacks ever bred have red eyes. Hens sometimes have black eye colour but these are suspect and have usually been bred from Greys.

Whites may also be bred pure but they are not as easy as Blacks. Many of the best Whites are sports, mainly from Black Tailed Whites and Buffs. Unless one buys Whites from a consistent stud disappointments may follow. Make sure you see the entire stud before you buy Whites.

Fig. 5.8 **Black Japanese Cockerel.** (*Owner/breeder*: M.E. Wingate, *photo courtesy*: *Poultry World*).

This is a variety that is troubled with green coloured legs; not eligible for exhibition. Strains differ in colour; one strain may have wonderful white colour overall, another may carry a large amount of brass or yellow in the plumage. I am referring to birds bred under similar conditions, shaded from the sun and deprived of any yellow corn in the feeding. Whites are usually of good type and low carriage.

Blue Japanese may be bred from Blacks and Greys. Birds bred from Blacks are mostly a dark slate colour and many are laced on the edge of the feather. Blues bred from Greys are usually lavender blue of various shades. I believe some of these could be invaluable in the breeding of Cuckoo Japanese.

Mottleds

Mottled Japanese are classified in three colours — Black, Blue and Red. They are a lovely variety and are usually of wonderful type. Blacks and Blues I recognise, though once again I confess I have never seen a Red Mottled Japanese. Some years ago I did form a strain of Buff Mottleds, but I unfortunately lost these in a serious fire.

Cuckoos

Cuckoo coloured Japanese have been seen at the last few Club Shows and they are quite pretty. Type is not up to the standard of some of the more popular varieties but, under the right management, could very soon be an example of the breed. Beware of any white in leg colour as this could be the result of a Scots Dumpy cross.

Fig. 5.9 **White Japanese Cockerel.** Best young bird at the Japanese Club Show, 1979. (*Courtesy:* Mr. F. Kemp, *photo: Poultry World*).

Fig. 5.10 **Cuckoo Japanese.** (*Courtesy:* Mr. F. Kemp, *photo: Poultry World*).

Black Tailed Whites

Other colours are few and far between and very rarely seen, if ever. There is, however, one more variety *par excellence*, the **Black Tailed White**. The demand for this variety quite outnumbers the rest put together. I sometimes wonder if some fanciers realise that there are any other varieties in Japanese besides Black Tailed Whites. Visitors seem surprised when I ask what colours do they require — "Black Tailed Whites, of course!". Their surprise is intensified when they view the stock.

Fig. 5.11 **Pair of White Japanese.** From a drawing by Harrison Weir, c. 1900. These are interesting from an historical point of view but do not conform to today's type.

I must admit it is also my favourite; none catches the eye more than this variety of Japanese bantam. Most popular in Britain, U.S.A. and Japan; for anyone with patience and a flair for the unusual the Black Tailed White is the one to please.

Many breeders of the past have been insistent on the tail and furnishing lacing and even now in the south of England this point is much coveted. Although I also admire a good clear white edging to the black tail furnishings, the ideal is very rarely seen. Black Tailed Buffs are much clearer and defined in this respect.

However, to me the pure black tail and furnishings on a pure white body plumage is far more striking and it is obvious when anyone views my stock which type they too prefer. The contrast between the black and the white is so pronounced that it catches the eye immediately. No matter what part of the country they come from, the would-be purchaser always plumps for the latter type. After all it is called the Black Tailed White.

It has often been said that there is nothing nicer than a good Japanese but, at the same time, there is nothing worse than a bad one. This is never more true than with this variety. Many poultry fanciers have an eye for a good Black Tailed White. There is nothing easier than to breed inferior Black Tailed Whites; quite another to breed what one requires.

It may take some time to build your strain of Black Tailed Whites but once achieved it is worth all the effort. To see a flock of these grand little birds is something a fancier will never forget; definitely the variety of Japanese for the connoisseur.

Fig. 5.12 **Black Tailed White Japanese.**

COLOUR IN CHICKS

The colour of chick plumage may vary considerably during its first few months of growth.

Black Tailed Whites

Taking the Black Tailed White first; chicks may be born with down plumage ranging from deep yellow colour to pale buff. Some may also be covered with an abundance of fluff, others may be so sparsely feathered as to be practically bald. Either of these types would eventually turn out successfully, colourwise, as adults or, just as easily, either could turn out equally poor. Nevertheless, whether good or bad in colour at maturity, both could be of the utmost importance as potential breeders, even though not of exhibition standard.

At approximately two months old, as the first feather begins to form, plumage may alter. Pigment may be very pronounced in some chicks whilst others may be devoid of almost all colour, some being nearly white. This situation may be reversed in the adult feather so it would be wise not to be too hasty in dispensing with birds that do not appear up to standard at this stage.

It is very easy to assess type but colour is rather elusive. It may be genetically possible to reach the required colour but by this time type has been lost and many other properties besides.

Type Before Colour

Any chick, however, that does not come up to standard in

63

type should never be considered for breeding, even though its colour may be everything that is desired. Colour should always come secondary to type and the breeder must remember to bear this in mind.

Black Reds

Black Red chicks are of the familiar striped pattern; i.e. brown line down centre of back from beak to tail, flanked by darker, narrower lines. These may be dark or light, the darker ones usually turn out cocks although some of these could eventually be excellent hens. The light coloured chicks are more often than not broken in markings and when matured are not up to the standard of their darker coloured brethren.

Males are lacking in sound wing bays and the required black breasts are streaked with red. Females come too pale in plumage with insufficient ticking after the first season.

Wheaten Black Reds

Wheaten chicks differ in colour sexually; males are a paler edition of Partridge Black Reds: females are cream coloured with buff tails.

Select male chicks with unbroken back markings and females as pale in colour as possible.

Crow-Wings

Crow-Wing male chicks are born with very dark Partridge Black Red markings. Females are born black all over.

Blue Reds

Blue Reds are similar to Partridge Black Reds, blue substituting for black. Chicks with broken markings should not be used in breeding pen if good coloured and well-marked birds are the aim.

Brown Reds

Brown Red chicks are all born with black down plumage and yellow or cream breasts. If occasionally the odd one is born with slight orange ticking on the neck this is an indication of a cross with some other variety of Japanese; i.e. Buff.

In true Brown Reds the colour only begins to appear about fourteen days after hatching as the first feather begins to form. The deaf ears are the first to colour followed by the breast feathers.

A further indication of foreign blood is that, when the birds reach maturity, the males' breasts will be suffused with buff and colour appears on wing ends which should be black. Females come with black caps and broken breast lacing.

Birchen Greys

Grey chicks are similar to Brown Reds. The true Birchen Greys are born black, both sexes, with smoke grey or creamy coloured breasts. Greys that finish with black or mealy breasts and light females with lacing all over the body are crossed with other varieties, Black Tailed Whites etc.,

Fig. 5.13 **Colour in Chicks.** This Black Tailed White hen is defending a mixed clutch of chicks, one being a Black Tailed White, the others Birchen Grey. All are three weeks old.

and should be avoided.

The real factors that determine true Greys are clear caps and breast lacing in female.

Buffs

Buff chicks vary in colour from cream to nankin in down plumage. Any shade is desirable even though the adult plumage may finish entirely differently to the baby down colour. Buff chicks that are born with dark markings may turn out to be the most clean and even shade as adults. Black pigment should be in evidence as soon as possible in wings and tail.

Blacks

Black chicks usually hatch out with white in their down plumage. Chicks born with all black plumage will seldom finish up a brilliant black. The more white in the plumage of black chicks at a day old, the better they are as adults.

Whites

There is a great deal of difference in the colour of white chicks even if from the same strain. It is very rare to see a Japanese chick hatch out a pure white. White chicks hatch out in various shades of yellow, cream and even of a blue-grey tinge. It is pointless trying to predict which colour turns out the best as adult, as they all could. I usually find

Fig. 5.14 **Assessing Plumage.** These two month old chicks are beginning to show their first feather so a rough assessment of their colour can be carried out. However, their plumage may alter again before maturity so it is unwise to dispense with birds that are not up to standard at this stage.

that the cream coloured chicks, especially with blue under-colour at a few weeks old, eventually end up as the best whites.

Of course, strains differ immensely and environment can play a big part in the down colour of chicks.

Leg and Eye Colour

The colour of legs and eyes in baby Japanese may be any shade or colour.

Feeding and environment play a big part in eye colour. Only three eye colours should be allowed in Japanese bantams: red, orange and black.

Leg colour in chicks is very unpredictable and no set pattern materialises with colour of plumage. However, the colour of legs to aim for is yellow or shaded yellow. Green legs are most objectionable.

Fig. 6.1 **The Ideal Mother.** Here we see a Birchen Grey hen on her eggs; the food and water containers must be present at all times whilst the hen is broody.

Plate 3

A Silver Duckwing
B Pile

C Cuckoo
D Tri-Coloured

Plate 4

A Large-Combed Black Tailed White C Pinch-Tailed Black
B Dark-Faced Black   D Dark Grey

CHAPTER 6

Breeding and Strain Making

A Japanese bantam is not a bantam capable of improvement by the introduction of an alien cross. For its development and advancement we must depend on the variety itself. Therefore, it is inevitable that we must only breed within the breed. Inbreeding is necessary and a "must" in most cases, but there can be a limit to this.

It should be the aim of every true fancier to have their own strain; this, however, is very rarely seen in the poultry Fancy. At least 80% buy birds here and there, not knowing if they were even bred by the person from whom they purchased them.

INBREEDING

The best way to form one's own strain is to obtain stock from at least two already recognised strains. These must then be blended together until the resultant stock are of high quality, possessing certain distinguishing characteristics unique to the stud. Not only must the birds resemble each other in appearance but they must also possess the power to transmit these virtues consistently to their progeny. Unless inbreeding is practised, however, this cannot be accomplished.

The breeder must devise a system and keep strict records of all pairings. By blending the good points together and eliminating the bad ones it should be obvious that unless the birds are inbred a strain cannot be formed.

Many breeders of livestock, even in these modern times, still condemn inbreeding, largely because of the fact that the human race is not allowed to do so by law. Others, who decry inbreeding, practise it and do not realise they are doing so. It is surprising how many think that inbreeding means mating brother and sister. Inbreeding means to breed in the points so desired irrespective of the relationship of the pairing. Only by breeding blood relations can this be achieved.

Furthermore, brother and sister mating is rarely used as this is stalemate and one can go no further. In the early stages of forming a strain, brother and sister mating is a good test mating. You will not, however, breed anything better from this pairing. If the breeder wishes to retain the quality of the brother and sister then there is no reason why he cannot do so by pairing their offspring together and so on.

Many fanciers inbreed without realising it. The only way to avoid inbreeding is to purchase fresh birds each year. No-one in their right mind will fail to breed from any of his stock that are up to the standard of excellence. The moment someone commences to use birds of their own breeding they are inbreeding.

I have a rule when breeding my birds. I never use any bird that does not either equal or better its parents. Only by this method can any progress be made.

Above all, there must at all times be no bird used in the breeding programme unless it is 100% fit and devoid of any physical weakness. Selection and elimination must be the aim when inbreeding at all times.

Line Breeding

Another form of inbreeding is line breeding. An example of this is where all the females of the stud are paired back to an outstanding male. This can be continued until a son of the cock, who is of equal merit, is used as the cornerstone of the stud. The ideal bird required to head the stud is a prepotent male. This is a bird that stamps all his properties on his progeny. This is the sire that all poultry fanciers are looking for, but it is very hard to come by.

However, it does not matter which method of inbreeding is adopted, one must cut out entirely from the breeding pen any bird showing the slightest sign of any weakness or ill-health. The use of any bird that is not in the peak of condition when inbreeding is fatal.

It has been said that inbreeding causes deformities and weakness. Actually, inbreeding brings to the surface what is lying dormant and it is then up to the clever breeder to sift the wheat from the chaff. By eliminating the unwanted factors and retaining what is required, the stock should, by the end of three seasons, be producing birds of the appropriate *standard*. There may be setbacks but there should be no call for panic and, if common sense prevails, these unwanted obstacles can be overcome.

There is no finer sight in the world than to see a thoroughbred Shire stallion or a Pedigree Shorthorn bull, both an example of what inbreeding can do. Our

Fig. 6.2   A Range of Breeding Pens.

racehorses and dogs seen at Crufts are other examples of what line breeding and inbreeding can do for pedigree livestock.

Once the breeder has established his strain he should be able to see the perfect bird. Though all the required points of excellence may not necessarily be on the one bird, nevertheless, they should be obvious in the entire stud. It should be the endeavour of the breeder to wrap all the good points together on the one bird. Only by the practise of inbreeding and line breeding can this be accomplished. Remember one can get out of a strain of animals or birds only what one puts into it.

There has been much controversy between poultry fanciers as to which sex is the most important in forming a strain. I have known many fanciers pay large sums of money for cocks that have done a considerable amount of winning in exhibitions and then put them to hens of little merit. In cattle breeding they say that the bull is half the herd and the same may be said for poultry. The cock is half the strain but remember that the hen is the other half.

It has been suggested that the male Japanese bantam influences colour and the female the shape. It is my experience that this only applies when new or fresh blood is used. Once the strain is established the influence of type, colour and size, is distributed equally amongst the sexes.

When your stud is established you may proceed, as mentioned, in the beginning by introducing a female with any point in which the stud is deficient.

I have often been asked how much length of leg is required to guarantee fertility. If all you require is fertility then go ahead and use long-legged birds, but my advice is to use the shortest and thickest legged birds you can get. It is better to breed a dozen really good short-legged birds than fifty that are not quite so good.

By the laws of Mendelism there can be no such thing as a pure, short-legged Japanese bantam. All Japanese which survive after hatching are split for short and long leg or long leg pure. When two short leg genes come together the resultant chicks either die in the last stages of incubation or soon after hatching (approximately 25%). Birds which are born with short legs and survive carry the genes for both short leg (visible) and long leg (invisible). Birds born with long leg carry the gene for long leg pure.

Japanese which carry the factor for long leg pure mated together will never breed anything but long leg chicks, so the use of such birds is pointless. Short leg birds which carry the factor for both short and long leg, paired to long leg pure birds, could throw 25% short leg or long leg and 75% long leg birds in the first generation, though none of the chicks carry the gene for short leg pure.

The best recommendation is to mate only the short leg birds to make real headway. Fertility will come if the birds are not harassed, no matter how short the leg. However, it should be noted that some breeders suggest using birds with *shorter* legs, but not necessarily the *shortest*. The only real danger of infertility comes from over-exhibiting and lack of aggression.

All birds should show the instinct to fight and to protect their families at all times. Any mature cock that runs from another or is cowed in any way is not suitable to be included in any breeding programme. Actually, I have found that Japanese females are far more aggressive than males.

IMPROVING STRAINS

Inferior birds are useless and not worth corn. They should be culled at regular intervals.

Many readers of this book will already be breeding some variety of Japanese. These may not all be up to exhibition standard. However, if you are short of some property in your stud that some other fancier's birds excells in, then by purchasing or borrowing a hen from the aforementioned stud you would set about introducing the needed property into your own.

Fresh blood would be introduced by a female if, for instance, the stock require only one point that it is desirable to improve. If the birds you own are lacking in two or three points then it would be advisable to obtain, or have the loan of, the best *type* cock you can find from a consistent stud.

Procedure

What follows may just as easily be applied to colour or any other property required, such as type. The procedure is as follows: put your best hens to the selected male and meanwhile scrap your own males as it would be pointless to use them again. Do not use any cockerels from this pen unless one is bred of better type than his sire. If this is the case, then do not use this cockerel the following year, but put some spare hens with him to keep him fit. In the meantime put all the previous season's pullets you have selected back to their sire. Select again the best type pullets from the resultant chick.

The following year put the best pullets back to their sire,

provided that the previous year's chicks are equally as good or better than the first year's chicks. In the third season you may now put half the second season's chicks with the first year's cockerel. This will give you half of the cock's blood on the cockerel's side and two thirds of the cock's blood on the pullet's side.

By working on these lines, which are a combination of line breeding and inbreeding, you should be able to build up your own pens of Japanese which will equal the best.

By the end of December the good stockman, having assessed the results of the year's breeding, should have cleared any surplus birds not required for further breeding or exhibition.

Try to retain birds for future breeding that either equal or surpass their parents in merit. Often it will be necessary to fall back on older birds to make up the breeding pens and endeavour to pair youth to age. This ensures vigorous chicks.

Females can be used for considerably longer periods than males provided they are active, have a bright clear eye, good head points and are firm in flesh. Japanese hens can be used until ten or twelve years old, but very rarely is a cock used who is over four years old. Second year cocks are best. Old cocks are useless, and often go groggy or tottery on their feet, drop dead at unusual times, moult badly or prove infertile.

Before continuing with strain making there are one or two points which should be mentioned here. Japanese are not a breed that require a cock and a few hens as in other breeds of bantam — many have tried this without success. Either breed in pairs or, if you wish to use more than one hen to a certain cock, it is best to keep him at stud and give him different hens on different days. Special males are kept isolated and only allowed females until mated, thereby ensuring complete fertility.

INCUBATION

Various methods of incubation are employed by breeders of Japanese. Over many years of experiment the conclusion reached is that nothing beats the "Jap". There is no substitute for broody Japanese. Game, Silkies, Silkie crosses and so on are alright for ordinary miniature fowl, but for the real tiny low chicks Japanese mothers are a must. Game are excellent broodies for their own chicks, but do not cover Japanese chicks for long enough periods at a time and tend

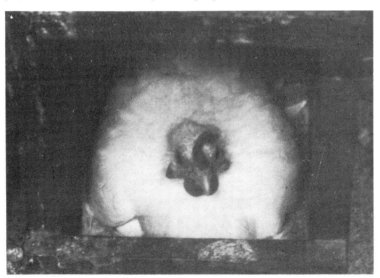

Fig. 6.3 **Broody Hen on Nest.**

to scratch the chicks about at birth. Silkies are apt to strangle Japanese chicks with their peculiar plumage, and they are excellent broodies, but rather dicey as mothers.

Artificial brooders and infra-red lamps are not to be recommended for Japanese chicks; these are forcing and draw the chicks up.

Contrary to the belief among many fanciers, I advocate that early breeding of all bantams is essential for the well-being and the continuation of the strain. Birds bred early in the year have the best time of the year in which to grow, and when the time comes for the first moult the weather is still warm enough for them to acquire their new plumage in comfort.

Many chicks bred late in the season could be smaller and low, but they are also low in constitution too. Late bred birds will never thrive like their earlier bred cousins. They usually hang in the moult till the following year and are actually a year behind. Late bred birds will breed the following spring, but the chicks bred from these birds will always be in trouble: moulting at the wrong time, blood quills, having rotten plumage and so on, and these defects may be passed on for generations.

Recently a Japanese fancier paid one of his frequent visits, accompanied by his friend who breeds Game. I also breed Old English Game so he likes to see how I have fared with the breeding. While in conversation about the Japanese this Game fancier said: "Yes, they look very nice, but you have to breed such a lot to have enough for exhibition". This remark amused me for the same person usually bred twice as many Game as I bred Japanese yet at the end of the year he never had any more show specimens than I had. Which once again proves to me my theory that the man who breeds haphazardly with many birds, relying on the law of averages that if you breed enough you must come up with something, does not always win.

It is far better to have a small select stud of good birds, to keep a strict record of every mating and to keep all birds in separate pens. Some poultry fanciers keep certain birds year after year that are not worth twopence for the simple reason that they are not sure which birds bred which. With the price of feed in this day and age, this is great waste.

Sometimes there is a certain amount of laziness on the fancier's part. It is far easier to throw food to a flock than to individual pens. This may be feasible with certain breeds of bantams but not Japanese.

DOUBLE MATING

It has often been stated that Japanese bantams do not require double mating and that exhibition specimens may be bred from the same pen. Actually, in many cases the breeder is practising double mating and does not realise it. Many fanciers select pens each year to breed birds of certain type and colour and so are unknowingly double mating.

Double mating may be defined in various ways depending on the breed of fowl. Rosecombs, Leghorns and Minorcas are double mated by pairing exhibition males to breeding females and *vice versa*. Partridge Wyandottes, on the other hand, have to be double mated, for colourwise they are really two varieties in one. Breeders of Old English Game have no problems on this score for even though double mating would certainly make a difference colourwise, in the end the poor coloured bird with the best shape would win.

81

Plumage

In the breeding of Black Tailed White Japanese there is a further consideration regarding feather which is a kind of double mating that is never mentioned in poultry breeding. Having studied carefully for over thirty years the Black Tailed White Japanese, I have come to the conclusion that it is similar in one respect to that charming little cage bird — **the canary**.

It has been generally known for a considerable length of time amongst breeders of canaries that these tiny birds have a plumage peculiarity. Canaries are bred with two types of feather; one yellow in colour, fine and close to the body, the other buff in colour with feather abundant and loose. These two types are referred to as *yellow* and *buff*: the actual colour of the birds.

After many years, breeders of that many coloured grass parakeet from Australia, the budgerigar, found a similarity in plumage. Now budgerigar breeders use the term "yellow" and "buff" to describe this feather quality even though in actual fact the birds may be blue, grey, green or any other colour.

Feather Quality

These two types of plumage can also apply to the Black Tailed White Japanese bantam. The ones I term "yellow" are tight feathered with whip tails, plenty of colour pigment and rather small in comb with short, thick legs. Birds referred to as "buffs" are very heavily feathered, rather soft in tail furnishings, lack colour pigment, are longer in the leg and much larger in comb.

The yellow type is most suited to the climate in Britain.

Fig. 6.4 **Plumage Variety in the Black Tailed White** – a fine pair of birds exhibiting tight feather and plenty of colour. (*Owner/Breeder:* Michael Thick).

83

The buff type has been introduced into this country frequently but finds it harder to adapt itself to conditions
experienced here and rapidly deteriorates in the wrong
hands.

To be really successful, these two types of Japanese
should be carefully blended together in the breeding pen, a
strict record being kept of all pairings at all times.

In the case of the canary, wrong matings could result in
the buff type becoming excessively feathered causing sores
and eruptions in the feather follicles, the yellow type wasting away altogether. In the Japanese bantam the opposite
occurs; the yellow type becomes unsuitable for exhibition
and the buff type becomes extinct.

With some experience these feather qualities may be
recognised by the observant breeder although this becomes
more difficult as the two types are intermixed, hence the
necessity for strict records.

At one period in time I really believed that these two
types were actually two different varieties of Japanese.
Now, after much experiment, I realise it was the difference
in feather formation.

FORMING A STRAIN

It should now be readily understood that in all breeding
programmes inbreeding and line breeding are essential.
Haphazard pairings and matings will get you nowhere.
Should you even chance to breed birds fit to win in the
initial stages, they will be worthless for future breeding and
the strain will peter out before it begins.

A strict record of all breeding operations must be

adhered to at all times. Many varieties of Japanese, though similar in type, cannot be bred on the same lines colourwise with success. If forming a strain of Partridge Black Reds for instance, line breeding is the best method.

The finest exhibition male obtainable, one of super type, colour and markings, is required to head the pen. The hens must be as closely related as possible and of true partridge colour. All the best females from these must be mated back to the sire; likewise their offspring. For at least four or five generations this programme should continue. By this time a cockerel equal to his sire should be kept for future breeding to carry on in a similar pattern. True Black Reds are among the most handsome of Japanese bantams.

Choosing a System

Buffs
When breeding Buff birds, however, another system must be adopted.

It is impossible to form a strain of Buffs with the even colour of Buff Rock bantams. If you were to use a male that was level in colour throughout, as advocated by other writers, with hens of a matching colour pattern for two or three seasons, you will wonder where your Buffs have gone.

Buff Japanese should be a deep golden buff, males having an iridescent sheen on the hackles. Both sexes must have as black a tail as possible with dark furnishings edged with buff. If light buffs of even colour be used in the breeding pen, pigment of points will disappear and body plumage will become mealy. White chicks will also appear in the resultant clutches. To attain the required colour in Buff birds, one must use various shades of colour in the breeding pen: dark to light, light to dark and so on.

A system of inbreeding must be devised that includes both sexes. Too close inbreeding with Buffs is not advisable; cousins, uncles and aunts are the best pairings. Again a strict record must be kept or otherwise your colour will fluctuate and may be lost. With Buffs it is advisable to use yearling cocks to older hens if possible.

For some strange reason in all strains of Buff Japanese bantams there is a weakness that is unaccountable. Although the Buff is the original variety of the Japanese, for some inexplicable reason birds that may be in the pink of condition one day may be found dead a couple of days later. There is no accounting for this but it is a proven fact.

Though the Buff is a variety that can be most heartbreak-

Fig. 6.5 **Black Tailed Buff Japanese.** Japanese Club show winners.

ing at times, when one sees a little Buff bantam with her brood of chicks running on the green grass of the lawn it is a sight never to be forgotten and worth all the heartaches.

Yearly Record

Date	Number of Birds Bred	
	Black Tailed Whites	*Colours*
19X1	16	20
19X2	18	16
19X3	22	14

Breakdown of Year 19X1

Black Tailed Whites		Black Reds		Buffs		Greys	
Males	Females	Males	Females	Males	Females	Males	Females
6	10	2	6	2	8	1	1

Brown Reds

Brown Reds are another variety of Japanese that require a different line of approach by the breeder destined for success with birds that follow the correct colour and markings. Other varieties of Japanese are sometimes necessary in the breeding of Brown Reds to achieve this.

Greys play a big part where the clearness of lacing is paramount. As already described these two varieties are similar in markings.

Birchen Grey pullets of exhibition standard may be mated to a mature Brown Red cock of clear lacing with pure black wing bays.

When using Grey or Brown Red hens or pullets, select birds with pure silver or gold heads; clear caps are very important.

Brown Reds may be bred from Buffs and Greys, though a great amount of culling may be found necessary before the true Brown Reds are formed. This may take some considerable time but, for anyone with an experimental flair, it can be very interesting. A pen of Brown Reds are a worthwhile addition to any Japanese fancier's yard.

Greys
Greys are a beautiful variety and, like the Black Red, line breeding is advised. Only males and females with clean laced breasts and black bays should be used where possible. Black-breasted birds may be used although these are best avoided if sufficient lace-breasted birds are available. On no account would I use the Mealy Breasted Greys. Although Grays may be used in the breeding of Brown Reds it is preferable not to reverse the procedure; I have never found birds with yellow in their make-up to improve birds of silver plumage.

Typical Example of Records Kept

Pedigree of each bird
Males above   Females below

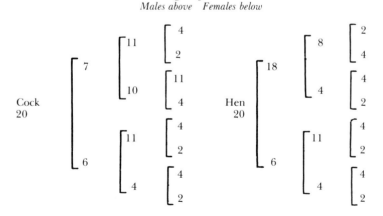

Piles

Pile Japanese are actually White Reds, having creamy white plumage where the Black Red is black. Unless one is fortunate enough to have a dilute mutation in breeding Black Reds, the chances of breeding Pile is very remote. If one could find a pure white strain of Japanese (which again is doubtful) then, by crossing with Black Reds, Piles may be produced.

Blues

Blue Red is similar to the partridge Black Red, blue substituting for black. Blue Reds may be bred from Self Blues and Black Reds, the resultant chicks being mated back to their parents. Best results come from Black Red males and Blue females, pullets being mated back to their sire. As blue is a dilute black, careful consideration must be given to the birds selected for Blue Red breeding. Clear coloured bays are a must in Blue Red cocks and any bird without these should not be used.

Lemon Blues have similar markings to Brown Reds and Birchen Greys, blue plumage being substituted for black. Again Blues mated to Greys could produce this variety; also a cross with established Blue Reds and Greys could have the desired results.

Lemon Blues, Birchen Greys and Brown Reds should have for preference mulberry coloured faces and dark eyes, though this would be very hard to come by in Japanese bantams, especially males.

Lemon Hackled Blues, not to be confused with Lemon Blues, are a distinct variety. The male has blue plumage all over, apart from neck hackle which is a clear lemon without any dark ticking. Body colour may be slate blue or lavender.

The female is similar to the male with clear lemon cap and hackle. The true Lemon Hackled Blue hen often has a suffusion of yellow in body plumage. Lemon Hackled Blues have red eyes and faces. Many Game fanciers refer to both varieties as Lemon Blues — very misleading.

Blue coloured Japanese are rare today. Actually, no real blue fowl exists. Blues are either a dilute black or, in Japanese, a lavender sport sometimes appearing in a clutch of Greys. The ideal colour of blue required in Japs is the colour of old fashioned roof slate. The exhibition Pekin bantam has the colour most sought after for Japanese.

A strain of Blues can be built up provided that Blacks are used in the breeding pens. Use Black hens to Blue cocks, and occasionally pair Blue to Blue. Undercolour should be noted; no bird should be used with white or black undercolour. Males with white quills in tail and wing should be avoided; plumage should be blue to skin. Birds with any brown or red feathers in their plumage should be eliminated from the breeding pairs. Breast colour in both sexes may be laced or self blue, either is acceptable in both sexes of Japanese bantams. Hackles in males will be darker than the rest of the plumage and the tails may be darker still or even black. Leg colour will need watching — very few have the required colour. If one was lucky enough to breed a White out of the Blues this would be a great breakthrough.

Mottleds
Mottled Japanese were originally called Spangles and even today some fanciers are confused by the two varieties. **Spangles are tri-coloured, Mottleds are bi-coloured**. Mottled plumage consists of a self-coloured ground with a white tip to each feather. The Japanese *standard* calls for each

feather to be tipped with white. If this was adhered to then the bird would appear too light for exhibition. If every other feather was mottled it would be nearer the mark. Both Spangles and Mottleds have one thing in common — both tend to lighten with age.

It is often suggested to balance the pairings by using dark birds to light. This can be very misleading to the would-be purchaser of Japanese. Matings should be based on first adult plumage; only at this stage is the true make-up of the variety displayed.

There should never be any need to lighten a strain of Mottleds, though it may become necessary to darken it. It is very easy for Mottleds to become too gay in mottling, this may be rectified by using a female the ground colour of your strain. It must be remembered, however, that Mottleds are recessive to other varieties so it may take a couple of seasons before the improvement of the self-blood becomes apparent.

Many years ago a breeder of Mottleds complained to me about the ragged plumage of some baby Japanese, insisting that it had not been caused by mice. (Mice do nibble bantam plumage if given the chance.) The first down plumage of chicks disintegrates as the first baby feather forms. This is more evident in the darker varieties.

FRIZZLES

The history of the Frizzle bantam that exists today in Britain is shrouded in mystery. I believe that this bird of unusual plumage is of Japanese bantam origin and has been bred solely for the frizzle feather. The short leg of the

Fig. 6.6 **An Example of the Frizzle Japanese.** (*Photo courtesy*: A.P. Hollemans).

Japanese being an unnatural feature, has been bred out, the normal leg length being retained.

As frizzle plumage was found to be dominant to normal plumage, it was an easy matter to *frizzalise* other breeds of poultry. It was also discovered to be of benefit to the Frizzle to incorporate plain feathered birds in the breeding pen; really good specimens are rarely produced without them. This also applies to the Frizzle Japanese bantam, now recognised in the British *standards*. If normal feathered birds (preferably Frizzle bred) are not used in the breeding, the result is loss of curl and feathers become narrow and stringy.

As long as I can remember Japanese and Frizzle bantams have been associated with each other. Many of the older school of fanciers, who sadly are no longer with us, usually kept both breeds of bantam and I know for a fact that they all crossed Japanese with their Frizzles.

C.A. House, a great authority on poultry and pigeons whom I had the good fortune to know in the 1930s, had, at one time, the only Frizzle bantam cock in the country. He stated that all Frizzles, white or coloured, were descended from that cock, and also that the Japanese was the only suitable cross for the Frizzle bantam.

If anyone wishes evidence of the similarity of the Frizzle with the Japanese, look at any strain of Frizzles that are allowed to run to seed. The resultant chicks usually acquire the Japanese type, bodywise, and this becomes more evident as they slowly lose their Frizzle plumage. If Frizzles are not selected for breeding for feather they may soon deteriorate. Likewise long-legged Japanese with Frizzle plumage may be mistaken for poor Frizzles.

In my schooldays I had a friend whose father kept Mod-

Fig. 6.7 White Frizzle Japanese Cock and Hen.

ern Game bantams, and being livestock "mad" I spent many hours with his birds, listening to his poultry lore. For as long as I can remember, up to the time of his death, he always kept a few Frizzle bantams on his allotment. They had wonderful curl of feather and the type of long leg Japanese. Every other year or so he introduced a normal plumaged, white Japanese female into his strain. I remember his telling me often that unless he did this his stock would lose feather curl and become very narrow in feather.

If one breeds a frizzle feathered bird in any breed of poultry then that bird is worth its weight in gold. It matters not if it be a strain of Pekins, Wyandottes, Japanese or any other breed of bantam or large fowl, this frizzled specimen from "out of the blue" is very valuable to the experienced breeder.

Over many years of observation of old poultry breeders it is surprising what they knew and very often kept to themselves.

Very often I have a Japanese chick born with lovely frizzle feathers that usually disappear with the adult moult when the normal feather is assumed.

Some years ago two or three leading fanciers of the day and myself had some lengthy discussions about Silkies and Silkie Japanese. A fancier named Pat Bloomer who was interested in poultry and pigeons, had just returned from a visit to that well-known Swiss breeder of Japanese, Dr. Renold. Dr. Reynold bred birds of the three different types of plumage and I gleaned much information from Pat. Billy Silk and Charlie Jones were among those fanciers present: all, alas, have now passed on.

SILKIES

Unlike the Frizzle, the Silkie feathered Japanese are recessive to all others, so unless one could purchase a number of these, preferably from the same source, it would be practically impossible to form a strain. Even though there is an established breed of Silkie fowl in Britain, I doubt if it would be much use in the making of Silkie Japanese. I have seen Silkies with pink flesh but still of the wrong type and with a dominant comb of the wrong kind.

Fig. 6.8 **Silkie Japanese Hen.**

CHAPTER 7

Exhibiting

In practically all books on poultry, what has been said is a repetition when the subject is one of exhibiting. The main theme has been to tell the reader how to wash the birds and what little extras they require, in the form of special feed, to warrant that extra shine on the plumage.

Fanciers learn most about shows — what is required and how to be amongst the prize-winners — from actually participating. The best approach is to enter birds and then visit the show and discuss birds with other fanciers. For the inexperienced fancier, the notes which follow should be regarded as the bare essentials.

SHOW PREPARATION

If a fancier is to be successful at shows, he should pay attention to the following:

1. **Show only fit and healthy birds**. The importance of feeding to achieve this has already been mentioned.
2. **Make sure that the birds chosen are show specimens**. Birds should be of the correct type and colour. Do not hope to win with poor specimens which have many faults.
3. **Give adequate preparation**. Birds should be quite

clean, and light coloured birds should be washed. In particular, pay attention to the following areas:

a) Vent — check for mites and their eggs; clean thoroughly — a small comb or brush may perform adequately without the need for washing.

b) Head and comb — wash and rub with a suitable oil or "preparation". (Many fanciers have their own recipe for the latter.)

c) Legs — scrub with a hand brush using soap and water.

If the whole body is to be washed, the bird should be immersed in water and washing-up liquid should be applied. After rinsing, the drying process should begin by the use of a hair dryer or, in hot weather, the sun may suffice. A towel can be used, to remove most of the water before the final drying commences.

Do not attempt to show a bird before the plumage is fully dried, otherwise the bantam will not look its best.

4. **Handle the birds and make sure that they are tame.**

SHOW ETIQUETTE

Showing is intended to foster a spirit of co-operation between fanciers. At the same time *friendly* competition is hoped for, thus attempting to improve the quality of the bantams being bred.

What is essential is for fanciers to behave in a manner which leads to better relations within the Fancy.

Whether winning or losing, fanciers should behave with

Fig. 7.1 **Handling Birds.** The correct way to handle a Japanese is to place the hand under the body, from the front, whilst clasping the legs between the fingers. The other hand should be temporarily placed on the bird's back. If this is done with confidence the bird will be completely under control and even the flightiest bird will remain calm and placid in the hand.

dignity. They should try to accept the judge's decision without complaint. **Obtaining a prize card should not become an end in itself**.

BENEFITS FROM SHOWING

In all forms of pedigree livestock breeding one should learn to walk before one can run. Not so today — many fanciers who become acquainted with the breed of their choice do so from a visit to some show or exhibition. In no time at all they have acquired stock and cannot wait to enter them at every show possible. This practice is not to be recommended.

This may be all right for fanciers with a deep pocket or those who are prepared to win prizes with someone else's birds but for the strain maker who prefers to exhibit birds of his own breeding, these tactics are out. It may take years to get to the top in an exhibition this way but, once there, not only is there the pleasure of winning with birds of one's own breeding but they are also acknowledged to be that fancier's strain.

To me the greatest achievement in livestock is to form a strain of animal or bird of top quality and for them to be recognised. I know of many exhibitors who, though they carry off many of the top prizes in exhibition, cannot sell more than the odd bird or two. I also know of many breeders of livestock who very rarely exhibit yet still sell every surplus bird and can never breed enough for demand. Personally, I would prefer to see a bird in my yard that could beat all others, and was of my own breeding strain, than fifty winners bred by others.

Fig. 7.2 **The Show**. A scene from a typical show where fanciers can meet to discuss important current issues.

Strain making can be a far more interesting, rewarding and relaxing hobby with true livestock fanciers than exhibiting.

One great aspect of all livestock shows is that they are wonderful "get togethers" for livestock fanciers from many places. Fanciers from far and wide can meet for a drink and a meal and indulge in comparing views and discussing important issues.

CHAPTER 8

Ailments and Diseases

Japanese bantams can never be a commercial concern, they are purely a hobby. They can hardly be considered a suitable choice for the commercial breeder who breeds poultry on a large scale as a business. In this instance veterinary aid to health in the poultry industry is essential.

Where poultry are kept in flocks of thousands, birds are subject to a far greater risk of infection than the exhibition fancier whose stud of birds rarely exceed three figures. Even so, the treatment of ailing birds in anyone's establishment is inadvisable and uneconomical in the long run.

If cleanliness and hygiene are up to standard, then disease should be rarely encountered. Thankfully, in this day and age, with modern veterinary medicines, diseases like coccidiosis, Newcastle disease and salmonella are not as prevalent as before. However, it is always wise to isolate any new birds purchased for a **safe period**. Likewise, birds returning from a show should be treated against parasites and disease. **Prevention is far better than any cure**.

Where Japanese bantams are concerned, unless due to the unforeseen negligence of the owner, all birds with any ailment, deformity or virus should be excluded from the establishment. If any bird should be subject to a sudden cold, but is otherwise healthy in every respect, then this bird should be given the chance to recover. If, however, any bird displays any sign of sickness when management is of the highest standard, then such birds should not be used for further breeding.

Anyone who keeps this breed and requires medicines and ailment cures is practising a form of management that leaves much to be desired. However, all penning rooms need a medicine cabinet, though the contents should be minimal. My own contains three bottles: one of iodine, one of antiseptic and another of Duramitex; a paint brush for applying the antiseptic and a towel.

White-Comb

Japanese suffer from "**white-comb**", sometimes wrongly described as favous (an entirely different complaint). Even under the strictest conditions of hygiene, white-comb affects certain birds, especially males, and occurs in a number of breeds of poultry with excessive combs. I have found the only real cure for this is to apply antiseptic, diluted with water for the young birds.

Accidents

Even in the most well organised poultry yard accidents can happen and do. Usually, most bantam breeders are employed away from home during certain hours of the day and at this time birds are apt to do unaccountable things. Strong winds may break a door off its hinges or a pane of glass may be blown out and damage the birds. Any number of things may occur.

Flesh wounds may be washed and treated with Iodine. With anything more serious it is up to the owner to decide whether it warrants the fee of the vet.

Scaly Leg

Scaly leg is caused by a parasite and only occurs under filthy conditions. The only real cure for this condition is to apply a mixture of paraffin oil and creosote or confiscate the bird in question.

Lice

Apart from the ravages of body mites at various times, the breeder of Japanese should have no further use for other ailment cures. Two kinds of lice are common to poultry: Red-mite and Northern-mite. The former come out of infested woodwork at night and suck the blood of the bird, returning to their hiding place during the hours of daylight. The Northern-mite lives on the bird itself and is introduced by vermin and wild birds, and is also passed on by infected birds at poultry shows.

Creosote is the only way to rid accommodation of Red-mite. To prevent any body mites attacking the birds I have found Duramitex, as advertised for pigeons, excellent and, once applied, it is effective for over six months. A twice yearly application is ample. Simply hold the bird by the wings with one hand, allowing the body to hang. Now push the web of a primary feather into the neat liquid and pass it twice over the underside of the open wing feathers, taking care not to touch the membrane of the wing or any part of the skin. I also wet the feathers round the vent and behind the neck with the feather. This has no effect on the birds whatsoever and I have used this method for many years.

Perch paint (nicotine sulphate) is also a good lice preventive for most breeds of poultry. This is now mostly a thing of the past, plus the fact that one has to sign the Poisons Register to obtain it. Owing to the fact that I do not advise perches for Japanese, perch paint is unnecessary.

OTHER COMPLAINTS

Many other diseases could be mentioned such as coccidiosis. However, for an explanation of these the reader is advised to study a specialised book. Fortunately Japanese bantams kept intensively do not pick up the germs as easily as some other breeds.

CONCLUSION

At the conclusion of this book I realise that I have been most fortunate to have been associated with this pleasurable hobby of breeding bantams.

Nothing can be more stimulating to the breeder of Japanese than to see his or her stock at the end of a successful season.

Fig. 8.1 **A Pair of Japanese** — these birds can provide a fascinating and pleasurable hobby. From a drawing by Harrison Weir, c.1900.

The years roll by endlessly; some good, some bad, but to the dedicated breeder if they only come up with one good bird the effort has all been worthwhile.

Bibliography

Bantam Breeding and Genetics, Jeffrey, Fred P., 1979
Book of Bantams, American Bantam Association, 1975
The Chabo and its Breeding, Inagaki, C., Tokyo, 1951
The Poultry Club Year Book, 1967

Index

Reference in italics refer to illustrations.

INDEX

for sitting hens, 35
Greys, 51, 53
   colour in chicks, 65, 67
   standards, 12
   system of breeding, 88
   use in breeding Brown Reds, 87
   see also Birchen Greys; Dark
      Greys; Silver Greys
Grit, 39
Grit hopper, *39*
Grower's mash, 35

Handling birds, *99*
Head, of cock bird, 8
Health requirements, 33–4
Hen birds, *9*
   breeding life, 78
   standard, 8–9
Honey Dun as secondary colour,
   14
House, C.A., 93
Housing, 21–8
   creosoting, 28, 105
   dimensions, 21
   hygiene, 27
   influence on eye colour, 69
   landscaping, 23–4
   large units, 22–3
   on concrete areas, 22
Hygiene, 27
   for avoidance of disease, 103
   of floor litter, 28–9
   of food vessels, 31
   of water supply, 40

Inbreeding, 71–3
   method for producing Buffs,
     86

Incubation, 79–81
Infra-red lamps, 80
Intensive management, 24
International Japanese Club, 7
Isolation of new stock, 103

Japanese Club Show, 4
Japanese Long-Tailed Fowl, 2, *3*
Jones, Charlie, 95
Judging
   avoidance of prejudice, 17
   characteristics looked for, 43
   overall considerations, 16
   stages involved, 16–17
Jungle Fowl, 1

Keel bone, effect of early
   perching, 31

Landscaping around pens, 23–4
Lavender Blues
   standard, 13
Lavenders, 57
Legs
   colour in chicks, 69
   colour not aided by damp litter,
     28
   correct type, 46
   defects, 9
   effect of split corn on colour, 37
   genetic groupings, 76
   judging points, 17
   length related to fertility, 75–6
   of cock bird, 8
   points available for colour, 14
   thickness, 46
Lemon Blues, 89
Lemon Hackled Blues, 89–90